STEAM
stories

THE GREAT GO-KART RACE

(Science)

Written by
Jonathan Litton

Illustrated by
Magalí Mansilla

The Great Go-Kart Race was about to begin.
Everyone was super-excited!
"Let's have a speedy start, a lightening-quick middle
and a furiously fast finish!" said Suzy to Max.

Professor Know-It-All lined them
up at the starting line.
"Are you ready?" he asked.

"5, 4, 3, 2, 1, GO, GO, GO!"

And in a cloud of dust, they were off!

"I know all about speed," said Max.
"Just watch this!"
He pressed **harder** and **harder** on the accelerator and the go-kart went **faster** and **faster**.

They made a great start and
zoomed straight into the lead!
All was going smoothly, until …

SPLAT!

They drove straight into a big muddy puddle.

"Oh no! How will we get out of here?" asked Suzy.

"Shall we **push** or shall we **pull** the go-kart?"

"I'll try to **push**," answered Max. "You take the wheel and run the engine on **full power**."

But Suzy wasn't sure. Could Max **push** the go-kart out of the soft, sticky mud all by himself?

Suzy pressed down on the accelerator.
VROOM, VROOOOOOOM went the engine
as the wheels turned round.

Splitter-splatter went the mud,
covering Max from head to toe!
But the go-kart wouldn't budge.

Luckily, Freddy the farmer came chugging along.
He tied the go-kart to the back of his big tractor
and **pulled** it out of the mud.

Yay!

"The tractor is a bit more
powerful than you, Max,"
laughed Suzy.

Suzy took the wheel. She was even
zippier than Max! She pressed down
on the accelerator and their yellow
go-kart whizzed through the countryside.

Before long, Suzy and Max were overtaking other drivers at every corner!

Soon, they came to a dark tunnel. Suzy couldn't see clearly so she pressed the switch for the headlights but ...

... nothing happened! She pulled over to think about what to do next.

"The lights aren't working!" said Max.
"What shall we do?"

"Hmmm," thought Suzy. "They need energy!
I get my energy from **food**, and these
sunflowers get their **energy**
from the **sun**."

Max laughed. "But headlights don't get energy from food or sunlight. They use **electricity**."

"That's right," said Suzy. "My torch uses electricity when I read at bedtime. And do you know what powers it? A **battery!**"

"Wow! Good thinking, Suzy," said Max.
"I think we have a spare battery.
Let's attach it and see."

IT WORKED!

The lights shone brightly when they changed the battery. Max hopped in the driving seat and they raced through the tunnel. They were in second place when all of a sudden ...

PSSSSSSS!

"What's happened?" asked Max.

Suzy looked at the wheel and said, "Oh no, it's a puncture! We can't drive with a flat tyre."

"Look, there's a garage over there!" replied Max. So they **pushed** the go-kart to the garage.

"Let's think for a minute," said Max. "We need to cover the hole." They found a puncture repair kit in the boot and patched up the hole in no time.

AIR

SAND

But the tyre was still flat. They needed to fill it up with something, but what?

Max asked, "What shall we use to fill up the tyre?"

"We could try sand," said Suzy. "But it will make the tyre **solid** and **hard**. We would have a bumpy ride on some of these roads."

Max thought for a moment. "We need something **soft** and **light** inside the tyre, to soften the bumps."

AIR

SAND

"**Air!**" they both shouted.
They pumped up the tyre and
hopped back into the go-kart.

How right they were!
Thanks to some daredevil driving,
they whizzed past two more go-karts,
and crossed the line to finish
in second place!

To their surprise, Professor Know-It-All declared they were the winners of the

SUPER SCIENTIFIC PROBLEM-SOLVING CUP.

It was even better than winning the race!

WELL DONE
SUZY AND MAX!

The science behind the story

Let's look at the problems Suzy and Max faced in the story. Turn to the page numbers for help, or find the answers on the next page.

p.9

p.8

Feel the force

Forces can move objects. They can also stop things from moving. Pushing and pulling are types of forces.

Why couldn't Max push the go-kart out of the mud?

Why did the tractor succeed in pulling the go-kart out?

Your turn

When you push a friend on a swing or pull open a door, you are using a force. Can you think of other ways you use forces at home, at school or in the playground?

Sources of energy

**People, animals and plants need energy
to live. Machines need energy to work.**

*What did the go-kart need to make
its headlights work?*

Your turn

Energy can be stored in a battery, or in food. When
you run, kick a ball, switch on a fan or launch a
rocket, you are using energy. What other ways can
you use energy?

p.19 Marvellous materials

**Air and sand are types of materials.
Different materials work better for different tasks.**

AIR

*Why did Suzy and Max use air to
pump up the tyre and not sand?*

Your turn

Materials have different properties which make them useful
for different jobs. Look at the materials that make up things
around you – at home or in school. Why do you think that
material was used? Would other materials work better?

Answers

If you need help finding the answers, try reading the page again.

Feel the force: The go-kart was too heavy for Max to push out of the mud. The tractor succeeded because it could apply a bigger force than Max could.

Sources of energy: The go-kart needed a new battery to power its headlights.

Marvellous materials: Sand would make the tyre solid and hard. The go-kart would not absorb bumps in the road.

Quarto is the authority on a wide range of topics.

Quarto educates, entertains and enriches the lives of our readers—enthusiasts and lovers of hands-on living.

www.quartoknows.com

Author: Jonathan Litton
Illustrator: Magalí Mansilla
Consultant: Ed Walsh
Editors: Jacqueline McCann,
Carly Madden, Ellie Brough
Designer: Sarah Chapman-Suire

First published in 2018 by QED Publishing, an imprint of The Quarto Group.
The Old Brewery, 6 Blundell Street, London, N7 9BH, United Kingdom.
T +44 (0)20 7700 6700
F +44 (0)20 7700 8066
www.QuartoKnows.com

A catalogue record for this book is available from the British Library.

ISBN 978-1-78603-278-2

9 8 7 6 5 4 3 2 1

Manufactured in Dongguan, China
TL052018

MIX
Paper from responsible sources
FSC® C104723

Find out more...

Here are links to websites where you will find more information on power, and pushing and pulling forces.

BBC Bitesize
www.bbc.co.uk/education/topics/zn77hyc

Science Sparks
www.science-sparks.com